Guess What It Is

HarperCollins*Children's Books*

First published in India in 2022 by **HarperCollins Children's Books**
An imprint of HarperCollins *Publishers*
Building No 10, Tower A, 4th Floor,
DLF Cyber City, Phase II, Gurugram 122002
www.harpercollins.co.in

2 4 6 8 10 9 7 5 3 1

P-ISBN: 9789356293823
E-ISBN: 9789356293830

Typeset in CookieRunOTF 14 pt/24 by **Shamika Chaves**

Printed and bound by Nutech Print Services – India

HarperCollinsIn

Ricky

MUHAHAHA! You may know Pang as the group leader, but the true leader is me! You'll understand if you stick around! HAHAHA!

Oliver

What great weather we have today.
On a day like this, I just want to sit by the lake, eat cookies, and listen to some music.
So... Please don't take my cookies!

Shasha

I can make anything I put my mind to! So tell me what you need.
But don't go asking for too much, okay?

PANG

I like anything fun! Join me if you are feeling down.
PANG! A game of cricket will help you feel better!

Cash

Let's go play right now!!
It'll be fun! Quickly!
Cash has lots of great ideas!

Cash was at Shasha's house.

He was helping Shasha organize her toys and gadgets.

"It's so much fun!" Cash shouted into a megaphone.

"It's a fun game we can all play together!" said Shasha.

Cash was very curious.

He quickly ran out to call his friends.

Soon everyone was gathered at the field.

"You can do it, Oliver!" Pang cheered.

Oliver had one hand inside the mysterious box.

He tried to guess what was inside, only by touching it.
Pang, Ricky, and Oliver tried their best, but it wasn't easy.

"It's bumpy and green!" Pang shouted.
"Is it broccoli?" guessed Oliver.

"Correct!" Shasha said.

Now it was Ricky and Cash's turn to play.
Each team had to guess the object correctly to win.

"Is he really going to touch that?" Pang cried.
Pang and Oliver acted scared.

Now Ricky was afraid to put his hand inside the box.
Soon the time was up and Ricky's team lost the game.

"It's not fair! Pang and Oliver made it very hard for me!"

Ricky shouted.

"This game isn't that hard!" said Shasha.
"Then why don't you give it a try?" Pang asked.

It was Shasha's turn to guess the object.
Pang, Ricky, Oliver, and Cash thought
of the perfect object to place inside the box.

Whisper

"Hehehe," they giggled.

"Here I go!" Shasha said.
She bravely placed her hand inside the box.

"Ouch! It bit me!" Shasha cried.

Shasha tried again, but it wasn't very easy.
"Could you give me a hint?" she asked.

"It has a tail!" said Ricky.
"It roars!" said Cash.

"Oh, I know!" Shasha cheered.

"**It's a toy dinosaur!**" Shasha shouted.

Inside the box was a toy dinosaur that could bite, roar and had a tail.

Everyone had fun thanks to Shasha.

The **Cricket Pang** series is a set of picture books with charming stories based on lovable animal characters. The overall theme of the books is cricket, which besides being a very popular sport for children, also lends a unique flavour to this series. Children will love the main character, Pang, and his bunch of friends. Each book highlights important values through engaging stories and endearing characters. With their simple vocabulary and sentence structure, these books are perfect for early readers.

Being patient!

Being fair!

Being fun!

Being kind!

Follow our **YouTube Channel [CricketPang TV]** for more Cricket Pang content.
(QR code on the back cover)